Life Sc

M000248491

Table of Contents

Answer Key in middle of book

The Five Kingdoms

Name _____

Scientists have placed all living things into five kingdoms.
The organisms in each group below represent one of the
five kingdoms.

Label each group.

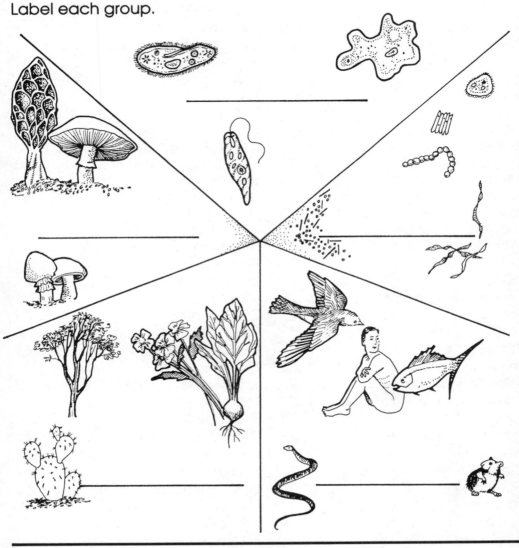

_____

_____

_____

_____

_____

_____

Word Bank

fungi	plants	protists
monerans	animals	

Family of Living Things

Name _____

Most scientists divide all living things into five groups, called kingdoms. Complete the chart comparing these kingdoms.

	Kingdoms				
	Animal	Plant	Fungus	Protist	Moneran
Does it make food? (Yes; No; Yes/No)					
Does it move about? (Yes; No; Some)					
How many cells does it have? (One; Many)					
Does the cell have a nucleus? (Yes; No)					

Animal or Plant?

Name _____

Most scientists divide all living things into five groups, called king-doms. Two of the largest are the Animal Kingdom and the Plant Kingdom.

Compare these two kingdoms by using the chart below. Check the correct box or boxes next to each characteristic.

Characteristic	Plant	Animal
1. Living organisms		
2. Formed from cells		
3. Cells have chlorophyll		
4. Makes its own food		
5. Gets food from outside		
6. Moves from place to place		
7. Has limited movement		
8. Can reproduce its own kind		
9. Depends on sun's energy		

Plant Parts

Name _____

Label the parts of the bean plant.

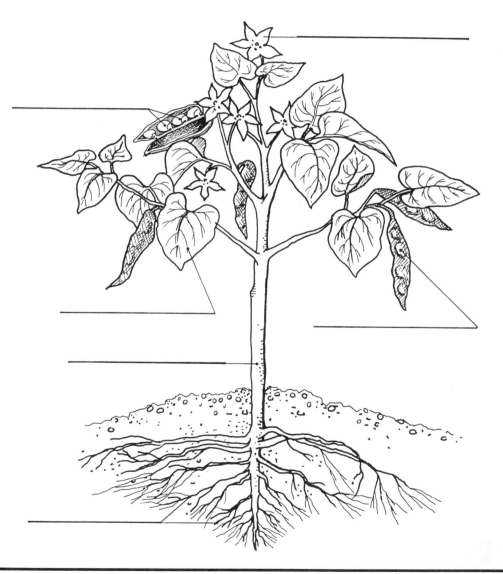

Word Bank

flower	fruit	leaf
root	seeds	stem

A Flowering Plant

Name _____

Label the parts of this flowering plant.

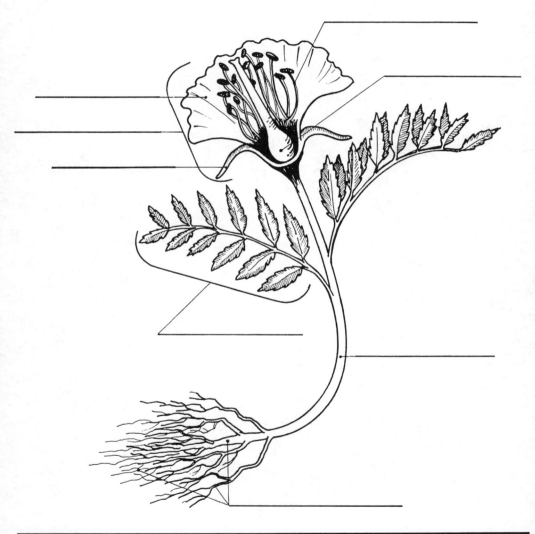

Word Bank

roots	stem	leaf
flower	petal	sepal
stamen	pistil	

Seed-Producing Parts of a Flower

Name _____

Label the seed-producing parts of the flower.

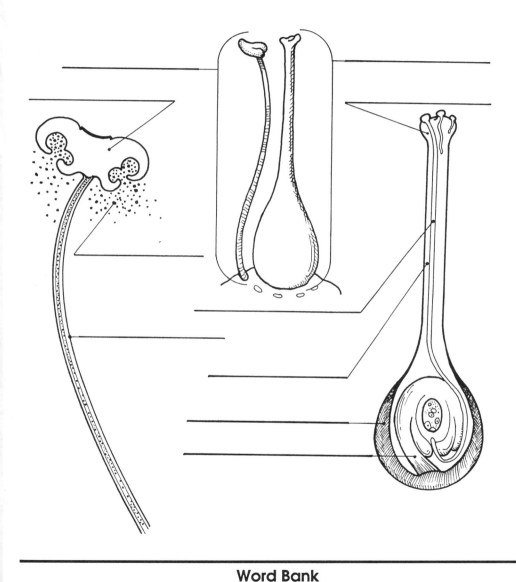

Word Bank

stamen	pistil	filament	pollen grains
stigma	anther	pollen tube	ovule
ovary	style		

Pollination

Name _____

Label the main parts that are involved in pollination. Label the two kinds of pollination.

Word Bank

cross-pollination	pollen grains	anther
self-pollination	ovary	pistil
stigma	style	stamen

Monocot or Dicot?

Name _____

Look carefully at the plant parts and describe the characteristic that makes the plant either a dicot or a monocot. Then label the plant part either dicot or monocot.

 Seeds Flowers

_____ _____ _____ _____
_____ _____ _____ _____

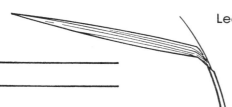 Leaves

_____   _____
_____   _____

Vascular Bundles
in stem

Roots

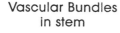

_____ _____   _____
_____   _____

Word Bank

1 cotyledon	parts in threes	fibrous
2 cotyledons	parts in fours or fives	parallel veins
net-veined	scattered bundles	bundles in a ring
taproot		

Eating Plant Parts

Name _____

Label the parts of these plants that you eat.

_____   _____

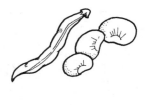

_____   _____   _____

_____   _____   _____

Word Bank

leaves	stem	seed	flower
fruit	bulb	tuber	root

Corn Grain

Name _____

Label the parts of the corn grain.

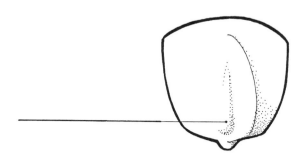

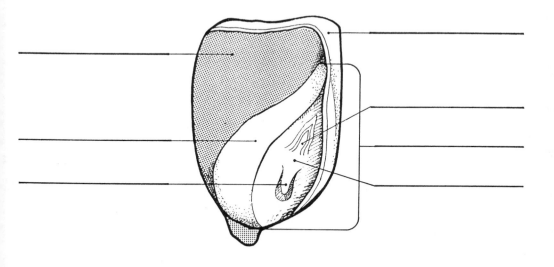

Word Bank

cotyledon (food)   embryo   seed and fruit coats
endosperm   epicotyl (leaves)   hypocotyl (stem)
radicle (root)

Bean Seed

Name _____

Label the parts of the bean seed.

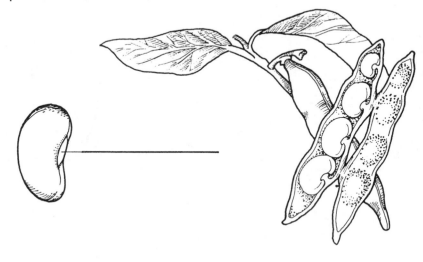

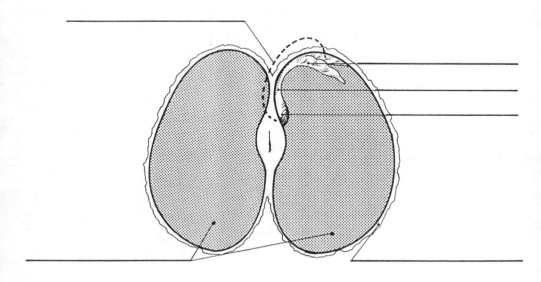

Word Bank

cotyledon (food)   hypocotyl (stem)   radicle (root)
epicotyl (leaves)   embryo   hilum
seed coat

Growing Bean Seeds

Name _____

Label the parts of the growing bean plant.

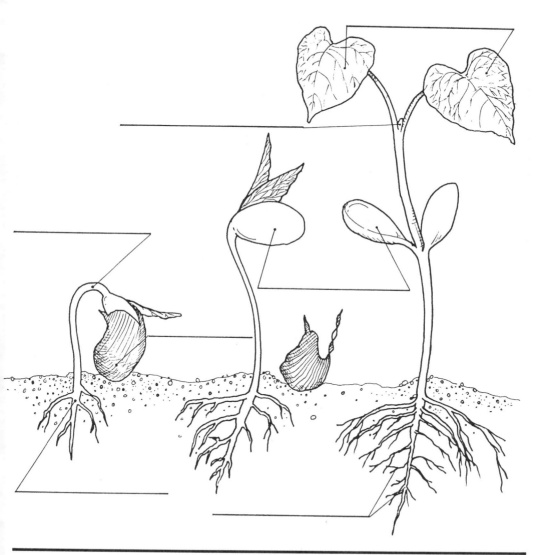

Word Bank

radicle   hypocotyl (stem)   cotyledon
seed coat   terminal bud   roots
first leaves

Tropisms

Name _____

Tropism occurs when a plant bends in response to outside stimuli such as light, gravity or water. Three common types are: **geotropism** which is caused by gravity; **phototropism** which is caused by light; and **hydrotropism** which is caused by water.

Label the type of tropism that is affecting each pictured plant.

Make a Prediction

The flowerpot in the first picture was placed on its side. The plant will continue to receive water and light. Draw a picture of what the plant will look like after three weeks.

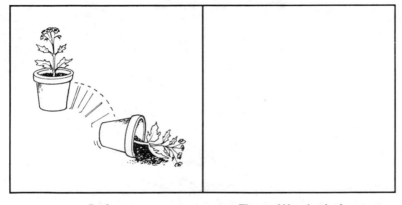

Before　　　　　**Three Weeks Later**

Traveling Seeds

Name _____

Seeds are dispersed, or scattered, from the parent plant in many ways. The pictures below show six examples of how seeds can be dispersed.

Explain how the seeds are being dispersed in each picture.

1. _____

_____

2. _____

_____

3. _____

_____

4. _____

_____

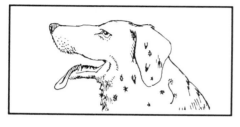

5. _____

_____

6. _____

_____

Food Factories

Name _____

Leaves are the "food factories" for green plants. Label the parts of the leaf.

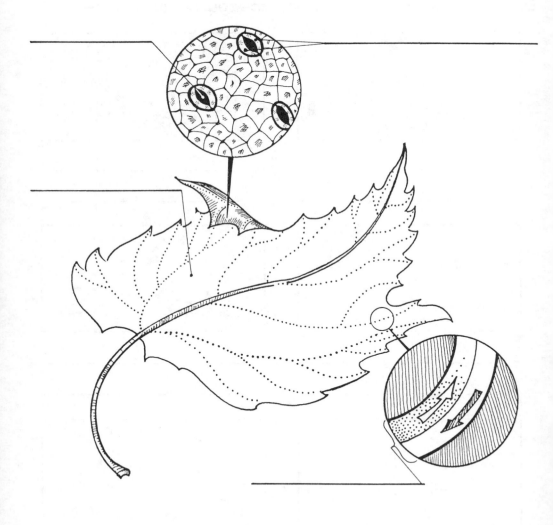

Word Bank

guard cells   waxy layer   stomata   vein

Leaf Cross Section

Name _____

Label the parts from this cross section of a leaf.

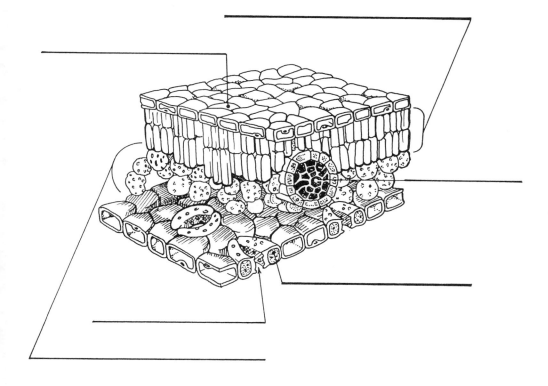

Word Bank

epidermis	stoma	guard cell
vein	palisade layer	spongy layer

Let's Look at a Leaf!

Name _____

Before you can use leaves to help you identify plants, you must know the parts of a leaf. Label the parts of the leaves below.

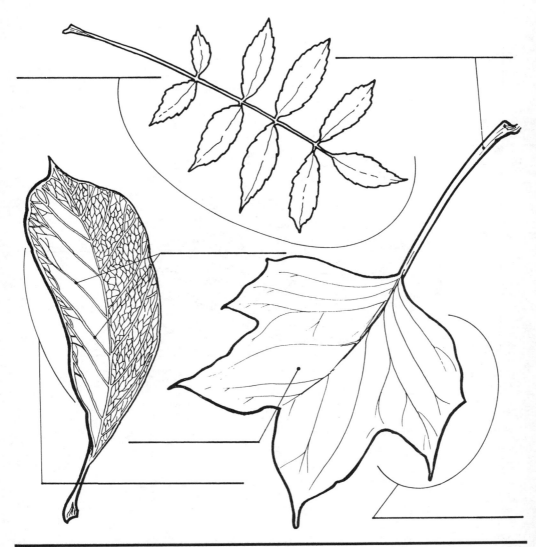

Word Bank

petiole	blade	margin
veins	lobe	leaflet

The Tree

Name _____

Label the three main parts of a tree and the types of trunk tissues.

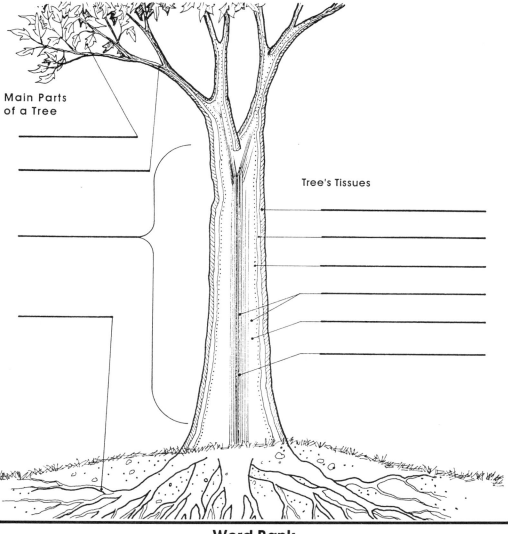

Main Parts
of a Tree

Tree's Tissues

Word Bank

leaves	phloem (inner bark)	heartwood
bark	sapwood	branches
trunk	cambium	xylem
roots		

Inside a Tree Trunk

Name _____

Label the parts of this cross section of a tree trunk.

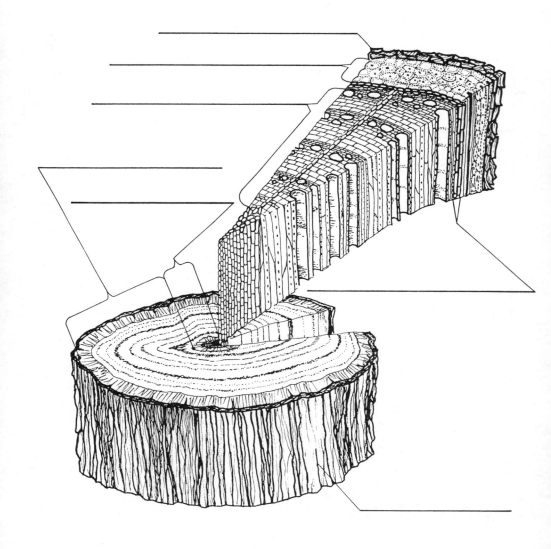

Word Bank

heartwood	sapwood	bark
xylem	phloem	vascular cambium

Underground Stems

Name _____

Tubers, rhizomes and bulbs are three types of underground stems. Label each of these types and their parts.

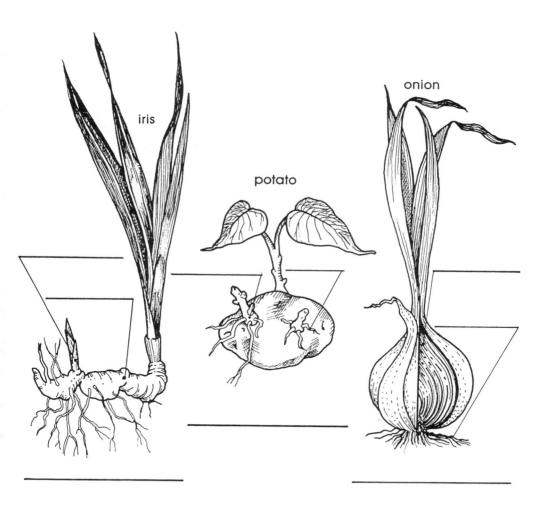

iris

potato

onion

Word Bank

bud   leaf   root
stem   RHIZOME   TUBER
BULB

IF0228 Life Science

Root Systems

Name _____

Label the two root systems pictured.

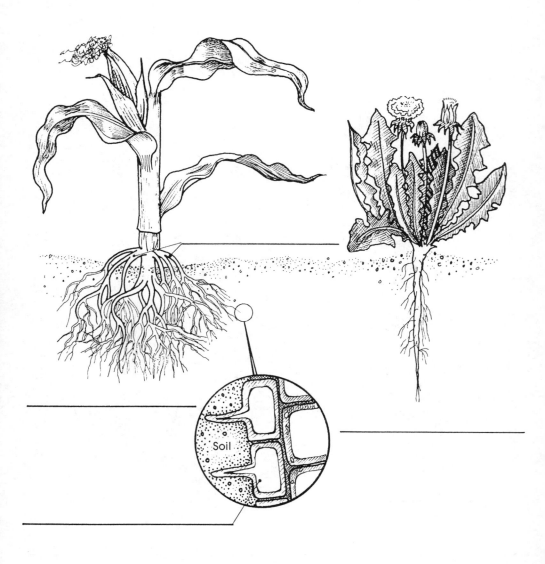

Soil

_____

_____

_____

_____

Word Bank
fibrous root system   root hair cell
taproot system   prop roots

Inside a Root

Name _____

Below are two views of a root. Label both the top cross section and side cross-section views.

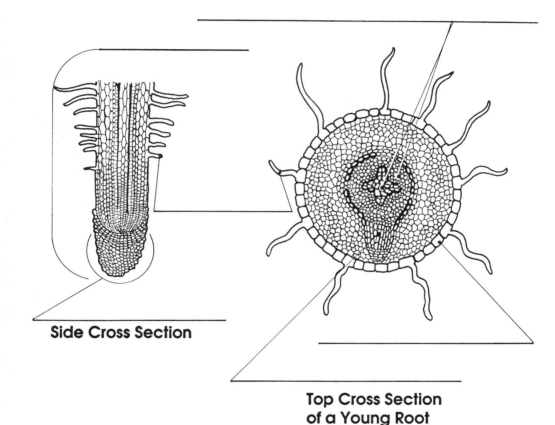

Side Cross Section

**Top Cross Section
of a Young Root**

Word Bank

root hairs	branch root	food and water
surface layer	root tip	carrying tissues
root cap		

Cycle of a Conifer

Name _____

Label the active parts in the life cycle of a conifer tree.

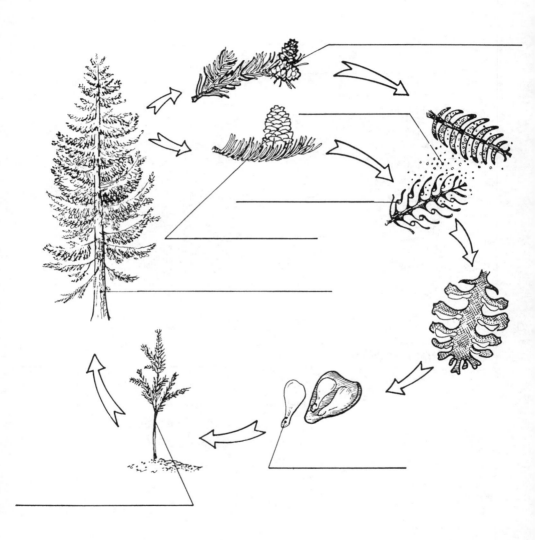

Word Bank

male cone	female cone	pollen
ovule	seed	seedling
mature conifer tree		

Ferns

Name _____

Label the parts of the fern.

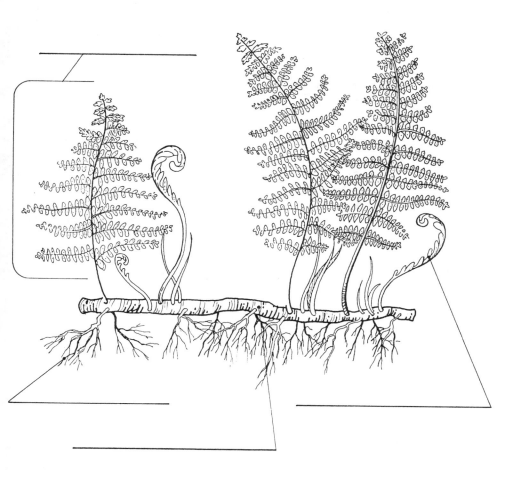

Word Bank

frond	fiddlehead
root	rhizome

Animal Kingdom

Name _____

The animal kingdom is often divided into subgroups called phyla.

Draw a line from each phylum to the animal that belongs in it.
Then draw a line from each animal to its characteristics.

PHYLUM	ANIMAL	CHARACTERISTICS

Flatworms

Segmented worms

Arthropods

Mollusks

Echinoderms

Chordates

Coelenterates

The body of these long animals is divided into segments.

The bodies of these marine animals have slimy plates with spines.

These animals have three body parts and jointed legs.

These animals have a noto-chord that supports the body.

These animals have soft, thin, flat bodies.

These soft-bodied animals are usually covered by a slimy shell.

These jelly-like animals usually live in the sea and have cylin-der, bell or umbrella shapes.

Animal Defenses

Name _____

Each of the animals on this page has a special defensive adaptation.

   a. Name the animal.

   b. Describe its defensive adaptation.

a. _____   a. _____   a. _____

b. _____   b. _____   b. _____

_____   _____   _____

a. _____   a. _____   a. _____

b. _____   b. _____   b. _____

_____   _____   _____

Word Bank

opossum	turtle	walking stick
ostrich	skunk	porcupine

Locomotion

Name _____

Animals have adaptations that allow them to move from place to place in a very special way.

Complete the chart by giving a one-word description of each animal's primary method of moving (locomotion).

Name the body parts involved in this movement.

	Method of Locomotion	Body Parts That Allow This Kind of Movement
rabbit		
fish		
mole		
blue bird		
spider monkey		
tree frog		

Symmetrical Critters

Name _____

There are three kinds of symmetry: radial, bilateral, and asymmetrical.

Label the kind of symmetry each of these animals has.

Animal	Kind of Symmetry
snail	
starfish	
jellyfish	
angelfish	
sea anemone	
frog	
sponge	
spider	
butterfly	
lobster	

Types of Symmetry

radial: The body parts are symmetrical around a central point

bilateral: The left and right sides are alike and equally proportional.

asymmetrical: These animals do not have a definite shape and therefore, do not have symmetry.

What's a Vertebrate?

Name _____

Vertebrates are often grouped into five different classes. How are these classes alike, and how are they different? Complete the chart.

	fish	amphibian	bird	reptile	mammal
body covering					
warm or cold-blooded					
habitat					
born alive or hatched					
lungs or gills					
chambers in heart					

IF0228 Life Science

Classy Vertebrates

Name _____

The vertebrates (chordates) are sometimes divided into **several different classes**. Name the class for each vertebrate.

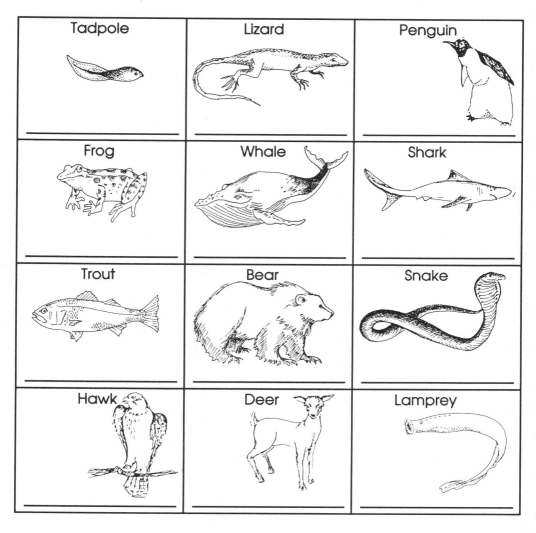

Tadpole	Lizard	Penguin
Frog	Whale	Shark
Trout	Bear	Snake
Hawk	Deer	Lamprey

Word Bank

jawless fish   amphibians   birds
cartilage fish   reptiles   mammals
bony fish

Vertebrates

Name _____

Vertebrates, animals with backbones, can be grouped into several classes.

List at least three characteristics for each of the classes below.

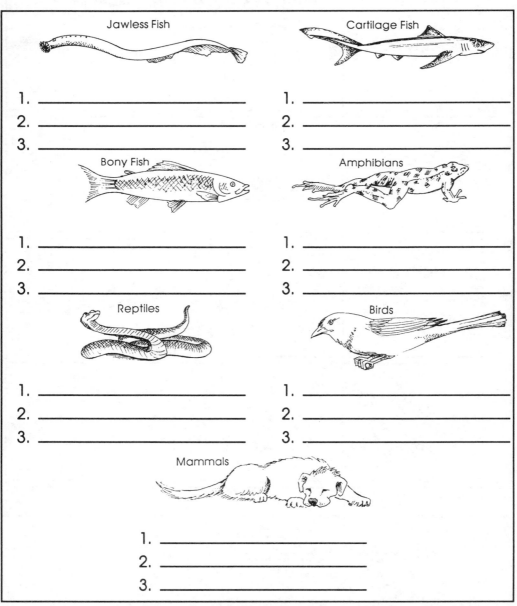

Jawless Fish

1. _____
2. _____
3. _____

Cartilage Fish

1. _____
2. _____
3. _____

Bony Fish

1. _____
2. _____
3. _____

Amphibians

1. _____
2. _____
3. _____

Reptiles

1. _____
2. _____
3. _____

Birds

1. _____
2. _____
3. _____

Mammals

1. _____
2. _____
3. _____

Backbone or No Backbone?

Name _____

Animals with backbones are called vertebrates. Those without backbones are called invertebrates.

Name each animal and label it as a vertebrate or invertebrate.

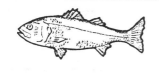

_____

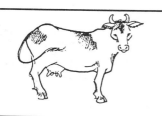

_____

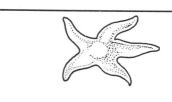

_____

_____

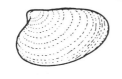

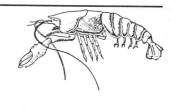

_____

_____

Word Bank

fly	crayfish	bird	starfish
cow	fish	clam	earthworm

Rippers, Nippers and Grinders

Name _____

Most mammals have two or more types of teeth: **incisors** for nipping food like scissors; **canines** for tearing food; and **molars** for grinding food.

Label the teeth on these animals.

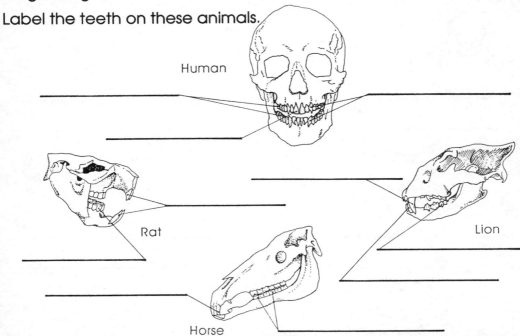

Human

Rat

Lion

Horse

Animal	Type of Teeth	Kinds of Food Eaten
Rat		
Lion		
Horse		
Human		

Word Bank

incisors	molars	canines
grains	grasses	meats
vegetables	dairy products	fruits

The Mammal with Wings

Name _____

Unlike other mammals, bats have true wings. But bat's wings are also like arms. Label the parts of a bat.

Word Bank

foot	tail	wing membrane
thumb	second finger	third finger
fourth finger	fifth finger	upper arm
forearm		

The Fish – Internal

Name _____

Label the parts of the fish.

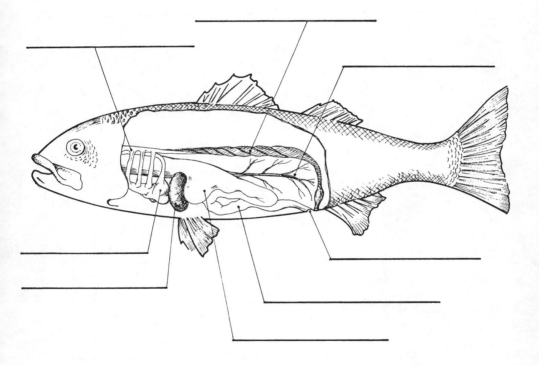

Word Bank

dorsal aorta	kidney	stomach
ovary	anus	intestine
liver	heart	

Answer Key
Life Science

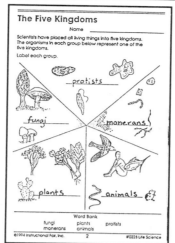

The Five Kingdoms

Name _____

Scientists have placed all living things into five kingdoms. The organisms in each group below represent one of the five kingdoms.

Label each group.

protists
fungi
monerans
plants
animals

Word Bank
fungi   plants   protists
monerans   animals

©1994 Instructional Fair, Inc.   2   IF0228 Life Science

Family of Living Things

Name _____

Most scientists divide all living things into five groups, called kingdoms. Complete the chart comparing these kingdoms.

	Kingdoms				
	Animal	Plant	Fungus	Protist	Moneran
Does it make food? (Yes; No; Yes/No)	No	Yes	No	Yes/No	Yes/No
Does it move about? (Yes; No; Some)	Yes	No	No	Yes	Some
How many cells does it have? (One; Many)	Many	Many	Many	One or Many	One
Does the cell have a nucleus? (Yes; No)	Yes	Yes	Yes	Yes	No

©1994 Instructional Fair, Inc.   3   IF0228 Life Science

Animal or Plant?

Name _____

Most scientists divide all living things into five groups, called kingdoms. Two of the largest are the Animal Kingdom and the Plant Kingdom.

Compare these two kingdoms by using the chart below. Check the correct box or boxes next to each characteristic.

Characteristic	Plant	Animal
1. Living organisms	✓	✓
2. Formed from cells	✓	✓
3. Cells have chlorophyll	✓	
4. Makes its own food	✓	
5. Gets food from outside		✓
6. Moves from place to place		✓
7. Has limited movement	✓	
8. Can reproduce its own kind	✓	✓
9. Depends on sun's energy	✓	✓

©1994 Instructional Fair, Inc.   4   IF0228 Life Science

Plant Parts

Name _____

Label the parts of the bean plant.

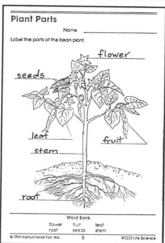

flower
seeds
leaf
fruit
stem
root

Word Bank
flower   fruit   leaf
root   seeds   stem

©1994 Instructional Fair, Inc.   5   IF0228 Life Science

A Flowering Plant

Name _____

Label the parts of this flowering plant.

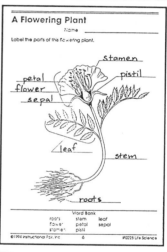

stamen
petal
flower
pistil
sepal
leaf
stem
roots

Word Bank
roots   stem   leaf
flower   petal   sepal
stamen   pistil

©1994 Instructional Fair, Inc.   6   IF0228 Life Science

Seed-Producing Parts of a Flower

Name _____

Label the seed-producing parts of the flower.

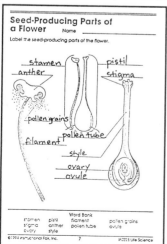

stamen
anther
pistil
stigma
pollen grains
pollen tube
filament
style
ovary
ovule

Word Bank
stamen   pistil   filament   pollen grains
stigma   anther   pollen tube
ovary   style   ovule

©1994 Instructional Fair, Inc.   7   IF0228 Life Science

Pollination

Name _____

Label the main parts that are involved in pollination. Label the two kinds of pollination.

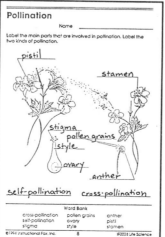

pistil
stamen
stigma
pollen grains
style
ovary
anther
self-pollination   cross-pollination

Word Bank
cross-pollination   pollen grains   anther
self-pollination   ovary   pistil
stigma   style   stamen

©1994 Instructional Fair, Inc.   8   IF0228 Life Science

Monocot or Dicot?

Name _____

Look carefully at the plant parts and describe the characteristic that makes the plant either a dicot or a monocot. Then label the plant part either dicot or monocot.

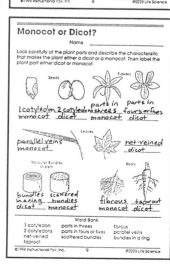

Seeds
Flowers
1 cotyledon   2 cotyledons   parts in threes   parts in fours or fives
monocot   dicot   monocot   dicot

Leaves
parallel veins   net-veined
monocot   dicot

Vascular bundles in stem
Roots
bundles   scattered   fibrous   taproot
in a ring bundles   monocot   dicot
dicot   monocot

Word Bank
1 cotyledon   parts in threes   fibrous
2 cotyledons   parts in fours or fives parallel veins
net-veined   scattered bundles   bundles in a ring
taproot

©1994 Instructional Fair, Inc.   9   IF0228 Life Science

Eating Plant Parts

Name _____

Label the parts of these plants that you eat.

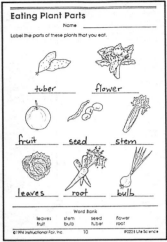

tuber _____ flower _____

fruit _____ seed _____ stem _____

leaves _____ root _____ bulb _____

Word Bank

leaves   stem   seed   flower
fruit   bulb   tuber root

©1994 Instructional Fair, Inc.   10   IF0228 Life Science

Corn Grain

Name _____

Label the parts of the corn grain.

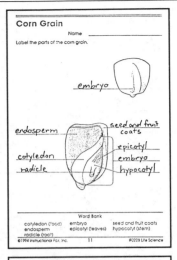

embryo _____

endosperm _____ seed and fruit coats _____
                  epicotyl _____
cotyledon _____ embryo _____
radicle _____   hypocotyl _____

Word Bank

cotyledon (food)   embryo   seed and fruit coats
endosperm   epicotyl (leaves) hypocotyl (stem)
radicle (root)

©1994 Instructional Fair, Inc.   11   IF0228 Life Science

Bean Seed

Name _____

Label the parts of the bean seed.

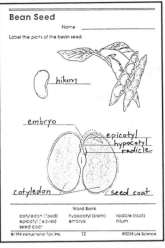

hilum _____

embryo _____   epicotyl _____
                     hypocotyl _____
                     radicle _____

cotyledon _____   seed coat _____

Word Bank

cotyledon (food)   hypocotyl (stem)   radicle (root)
epicotyl (leaves) embryo   hilum
seed coat

©1994 Instructional Fair, Inc.   12   IF0228 Life Science

Growing Bean Seeds

Name _____

Label the parts of the growing bean plant.

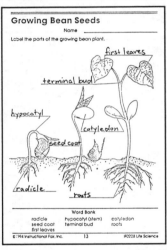

first leaves _____
terminal bud _____
hypocotyl _____   cotyledon _____
seed coat _____
radicle _____   roots _____

Word Bank

radicle   hypocotyl (stem)   cotyledon
seed coat   terminal bud   roots
first leaves

©1994 Instructional Fair, Inc.   13   IF0228 Life Science

Tropisms

Name _____

Tropism occurs when a plant bends in response to outside stimuli such as light, gravity or water. Three common types are: geotropism which is caused by gravity; phototropism which is caused by light; and hydrotropism which is caused by water.

Label the type of tropism that is affecting each pictured plant.

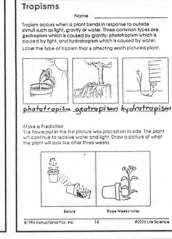

phototropism   geotropism   hydrotropism

Make a Prediction

The flowerpot in the first picture was placed on its side. The plant will continue to receive water and light. Draw a picture of what the plant will look like after three weeks.

Before   Three Weeks Later

©1994 Instructional Fair, Inc.   14   IF0228 Life Science

Traveling Seeds

Name _____

Seeds are dispersed, or scattered, from the parent plant in many ways. The pictures below show six examples of how seeds can be dispersed.

Explain how the seeds are being dispersed in each picture.

Possible answers.

1. Person plants seeds.
2. Squirrel plants a nut.
3. Coconut washes up on shore.
4. Bird drops seed from mouth.
5. Burrs stick to dog's fur.
6. Maple seeds are blown by wind.

©1994 Instructional Fair, Inc.   15   IF0228 Life Science

Food Factories

Name _____

Leaves are the "food factories" for green plants. Label the parts of the leaf.

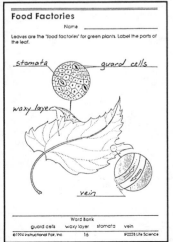

stomata _____   guard cells _____

waxy layer _____

vein _____

Word Bank

guard cells   waxy layer   stomata   vein

©1994 Instructional Fair, Inc.   16   IF0228 Life Science

Leaf Cross Section

Name _____

Label the parts from this cross section of a leaf.

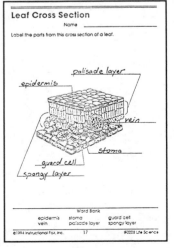

palisade layer _____
epidermis _____
vein _____
stoma _____
guard cell _____
spongy layer _____

Word Bank

epidermis   stoma   guard cell
vein   palisade layer spongy layer

©1994 Instructional Fair, Inc.   17   IF0228 Life Science

Let's Look at a Leaf!

Name _____

Before you can use leaves to help you identify plants, you must know the parts of a leaf. Label the parts of the leaves below.

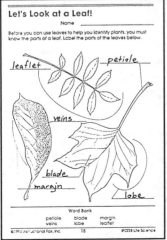

leaflet _____   petiole _____

veins _____

blade _____

margin _____   lobe _____

Word Bank

petiole   blade   margin
veins   lobe   leaflet

©1994 Instructional Fair, Inc.   18   IF0228 Life Science

The Tree

Name _____

Label the three main parts of a tree and the types of trunk tissues.

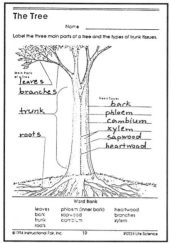

Main Parts of a Tree
leaves
branches
trunk
roots

Tree's Tissues
bark
phloem
cambium
xylem
sapwood
heartwood

Inside a Tree Trunk

Name _____

Label the parts of this cross section of a tree trunk.

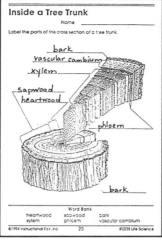

bark
vascular cambium
xylem
sapwood
heartwood
phloem
bark

Underground Stems

Name _____

Tubers, rhizomes and bulbs are three types of underground stems. Label each of these types and their parts.

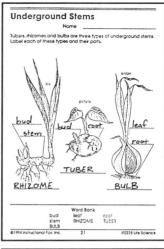

iris
onion
potato
bud
stem
bud
root
leaf
root
TUBER
RHIZOME
BULB

Root Systems

Name _____

Label the two root systems pictured.

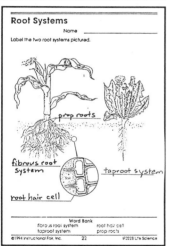

prop roots
fibrous root system
taproot system
root hair cell

Inside a Root

Name _____

Below are two views of a root. Label both the top cross section and side cross-section views.

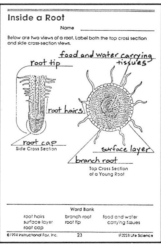

root tip
food and water carrying tissues
root hairs
root cap
Side Cross Section
surface layer
branch root
Top Cross Section of a Young Root

Life Cycle of a Conifer

Name _____

Label the active parts in the life cycle of a conifer tree.

male cone
pollen
ovule
female cone
mature conifer tree
seed
seedling

Ferns

Name _____

Label the parts of the fern.

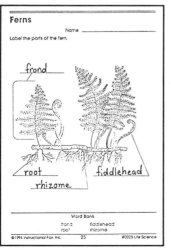

frond
root
fiddlehead
rhizome

Animal Kingdom

Name _____

The animal kingdom is often divided into subgroups called phyla. Draw a line from each phylum to the animal that belongs in it. Then draw a line from each animal to its characteristics.

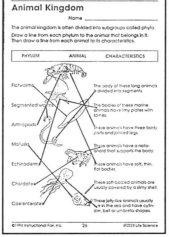

PHYLUM	ANIMAL	CHARACTERISTICS
Flatworms		The body of these long animals is divided into segments.
Segmented worms		The bodies of these marine animals have limy plates with spines.
Arthropods		These animals have three body parts and jointed legs.
Mollusks		These animals have a notochord that supports the body.
Echinoderms		These animals have soft, thin, flat bodies.
Chordates		These soft-bodied animals are usually covered by a slimy shell.
Coelenterate		These jelly-like animals usually live in the sea and have cylinder, bell or umbrella shapes.

Animal Defenses

Name _____

Each of the animals on this page has a special defensive adaptation.
a. Name the animal.
b. Describe its defensive adaptation.

a. turtle
b. hard shell for protection

a. skunk
b. spray offensive odor

c. walking stick
uses camouflage

a. ostrich
b. long legs for running; good eye sight

a. opossum
b. can play dead

c. porcupine
sharp quills

Locomotion

Name _____

Animals have adaptations that allow them to move from place to place in a very special way.

Complete the chart by giving a one-word description of each animal's primary method of moving (locomotion).

Name the body parts involved in this movement.

	Method of Locomotion	Body Parts That Allow This Kind of Movement
rabbit	hop	strong hind legs
fish	swim	fins and tail
mole	dig tunnel	shovel-like feet
blue bird	fly	strong wings
spider monkey	swing	prehensile tail
tree frog	climb, hop	adhesive disks on feet

Symmetrical Critters

Name _____

There are three kinds of symmetry: radial, bilateral, and asymmetrical.

Label the kind of symmetry each of these animals has.

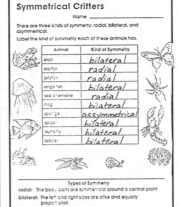

Animal	Kind of Symmetry
snail	bilateral
starfish	radial
jellyfish	radial
angel fish	bilateral
sea anemone	radial
frog	bilateral
sponge	assymmetrical
spider	bilateral
butterfly	bilateral
lobster	bilateral

Types of Symmetry

radial: The body parts are symmetrical around a central point.

bilateral: The left and right sides are alike and equally proportional.

asymmetrical: These animals do not have a definite shape and therefore, do not have symmetry.

What's a Vertebrate?

Name _____

Vertebrates are often grouped into five different classes. How are those classes alike, and how are they different? Complete the chart.

	body covering	warm or cold-blooded	habitat	born alive or hatched	lungs or gills	chambers in heart
mammal	hair	warm-blooded	land or water	born alive	lungs	4
reptile	skull or scales	cold-blooded	land and water	hatched	lungs	3
bird	feathers	warm-blooded	land, air and water	hatched	lungs	4
amphibian	smooth	cold-blooded	water and land	hatched	gills	3
fish	scales	cold-blooded	water	hatched or hatched	gills	2

Classy Vertebrates

Name _____

The vertebrates (chordates) are sometimes divided into several different classes. Name the class for each vertebrate.

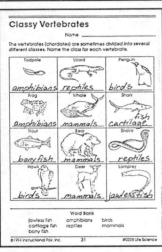

Tadpole	Lizard	Penguin
amphibians	reptiles	birds
Frog	**Whale**	**Shark**
amphibians	mammals	cartilage fish
Trout	**Bear**	**Snake**
bony fish	mammals	reptiles
Hawk	**Deer**	**Lamprey**
birds	mammals	jawless fish

Word Bank

jawless fish   amphibians   birds
cartilage fish   reptiles   mammals
bony fish

Vertebrates

Possible answers Name _____

Vertebrates, animals with backbones, can be grouped into several classes.

List at least three characteristics for each of the classes below.

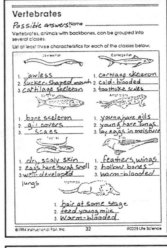

Jawless Fish
1. jawless
2. sucker-shaped mouth
3. cartilage skeleton

Cartilage Fish
1. cartilage skeleton
2. cold-blooded
3. tooth-like scales

Amphibians
1. bone skeleton
2. gill covers
3. scales

1. young have gills
2. young have lungs
3. lay eggs in moisture

Reptiles
1. dry, scaly skin
2. eggs have tough shell
3. well-developed lungs

Birds
1. feathers, wings
2. hollow bones
3. warm-blooded

Mammals
1. hair at some stage
2. feed young milk
3. warm-blooded

Backbone or No Backbone?

Name _____

Animals with backbones are called vertebrates. Those without backbones are called invertebrates.

Name each animal and label it as a vertebrate or invertebrate.

invertebrate
fly

invertebrate
worm

vertebrate
cow

vertebrate
bird

vertebrate
fish

invertebrate
starfish

invertebrate
clam

invertebrate
crayfish

Word Bank

fly   crayfish   bird   starfish
cow   fish   clam   earthworm

Rippers, Nippers and Grinders

Name _____

Most mammals have two or more types of teeth: incisors for nipping food like scissors; canines for tearing food; and molars for grinding food.

Label the teeth on these animals.

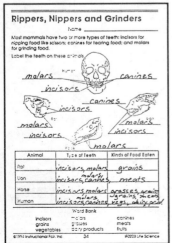

molars   canines
incisors

canines
incisors

molars   molars
incisors   incisors
molars

Animal	Types of Teeth	Kinds of Food Eaten
Rat	incisors, molars	grains
Lion	molars, incisors, canines	meats
Horse	incisors, molars	grasses, grains
Human	incisors, molars, canines	veg., dairy prod.

Word Bank

incisors   molars   canines
grains   grasses   meats
vegetables   dairy products   fruits

The Mammal with Wings

Name _____

Unlike other mammals, bats have true wings. But bat's wings are also like arms. Label the parts of a bat.

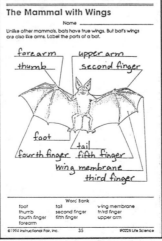

forearm   upper arm
thumb   second finger

foot
fourth finger   tail   fifth finger
wing membrane
third finger

Word Bank

foot   tail   wing membrane
thumb   second finger   third finger
fourth finger   fifth finger   upper arm
forearm

The Fish – Internal

Name _____

Label the parts of the fish.

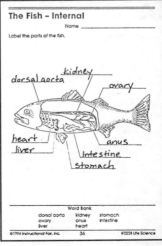

dorsal aorta   kidney   ovary

heart
liver   anus
intestine
stomach

Word Bank

dorsal aorta   kidney   stomach
ovary   anus   intestine
liver   heart

The Frog – Internal

Name _____

Label the parts of the frog.

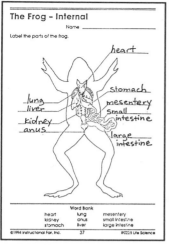

heart
stomach
mesentery
small intestine
lung
liver
kidney
anus
large intestine

Word Bank

heart	lung	mesentery
kidney	anus	small intestine
stomach	liver	large intestine

©1994 Instructional Fair, Inc.　37　IF0228 Life Science

Life Cycle of a Frog

Name _____

Label the steps in the life cycle of the frog.

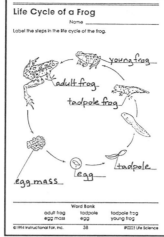

young frog
adult frog
tadpole frog
egg mass
egg
tadpole

Word Bank

adult frog	tadpole	tadpole frog
egg mass	egg	young frog

©1994 Instructional Fair, Inc.　38　IF0228 Life Science

Pit Viper Snake

Name _____

Label the parts of the head of the pit viper snake.

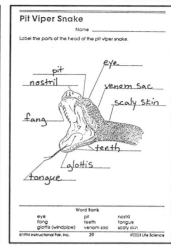

eye
pit
nostril
venom sac
scaly skin
fang
teeth
glottis
tongue

Word Bank

eye	fang	pit	nostril
fang		teeth	tongue
glottis (windpipe)		venom sac	scaly skin

©1994 Instructional Fair, Inc.　39　IF0228 Life Science

The Parts of a Bird

Name _____

Label the parts of the bird.

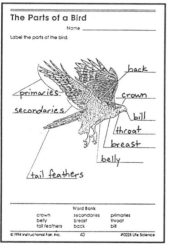

back
primaries
crown
secondaries
bill
throat
breast
belly
tail feathers

Word Bank

crown	secondaries	primaries
belly	breast	throat
tail feathers	back	bill

©1994 Instructional Fair, Inc.　40　IF0228 Life Science

Feathered Friend's Feet

Name _____

A bird's feet can tell you many things about its habits or home. How do each of these birds use their feet in a special way?

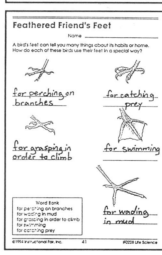

for perching on branches
for catching prey
for grasping in order to climb
for swimming
for wading in mud

Word Bank

for perching on branches
for wading in mud
for grasping in order to climb
for swimming
for catching prey

©1994 Instructional Fair, Inc.　41　IF0228 Life Science

Bird Bills

Name _____

The shape of a bird's bill can often tell what the bird eats. How do each of these birds use their bills in a special way to eat food?

to tear the flesh of animals
to suck nectar from flowers
to scoop large mouthfuls of water and fish
for pounding holes to find insects
to crack open seeds
to stab small fish

Word Bank

- for pounding holes to find insects
- to tear the flesh of animals
- to scoop large mouthfuls of water and fish
- to suck nectar from flowers
- to stab small fish
- to crack open seeds

©1994 Instructional Fair, Inc.　42　IF0228 Life Science

Strangers in the Night

Name _____

It's much easier to identify a bird when you can see its coloring, size and shape. At night this is usually difficult.
See if you can identify these birds by their silhouettes.

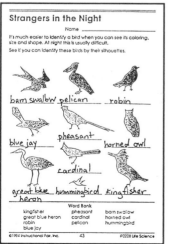

barn swallow
pelican
robin
blue jay
pheasant
horned owl
cardinal
great blue heron
hummingbird
kingfisher

Word Bank

kingfisher	pheasant	barn swallow
great blue heron	cardinal	horned owl
robin	pelican	hummingbird
blue jay		

©1994 Instructional Fair, Inc.　43　IF0228 Life Science

Highways for Birds

Name _____

Label each of these major flyways found in North America.

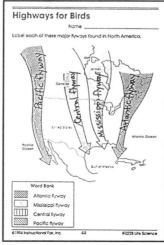

Pacific Flyway
Central Flyway
Mississippi Flyway
Atlantic Flyway
Canada
United States
Pacific Ocean
Atlantic Ocean
Gulf of Mexico

Word Bank

- Atlantic flyway
- Mississippi flyway
- Central flyway
- Pacific flyway

©1994 Instructional Fair, Inc.　44　IF0228 Life Science

Chicken Egg

Name _____

Label the parts of this fertilized hen's egg.

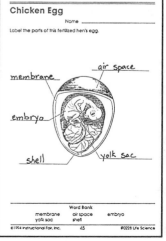

air space
membrane
embryo
shell
yolk sac

Word Bank

membrane	air space	embryo
yolk sac	shell	

©1994 Instructional Fair, Inc.　45　IF0228 Life Science

The Crayfish

Name _____

Label the parts of the crayfish.

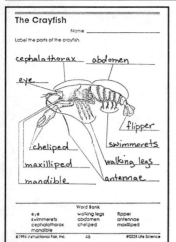

cephalothorax — abdomen
eye
flipper
chshelped
swimmerets
chehped
walking legs
maxilliped
antennae
mandible

Word Bank

eye	walking legs	flipper
swimmerets	abdomen	antennae
cephalothorax	cheliped	maxilliped
mandible		

©1994 Instructional Fair, Inc.   46   IF0228 Life Science

Insect Orders

Name _____

The major groups of insects are called orders. Below are examples from seven of the most common orders of insects. Label each insect and its order.

flies
Diptera

butterflies and moths
Lepidoptera

grasshoppers
Orthoptera

beetles
Coleoptera

leafhoppers
Homoptera

bees and wasps
Hymenoptera

true bugs
Hemiptera

Word Bank

- beetles (Coleoptera)
- flies (Diptera)
- grasshoppers (Orthoptera)
- leafhoppers (Homoptera)
- bees and wasps (Hymenoptera)
- butterflies and moths (Lepidoptera)
- true bugs (Hemiptera)

©1994 Instructional Fair, Inc.   47   IF0228 Life Science

Spiders and Insects

Name _____

Spiders are not insects. Label the parts of the spider and insect.

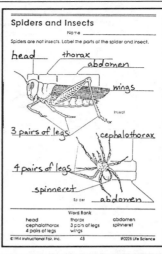

head — thorax
abdomen
wings
Insect
3 pairs of legs
cephalothorax
4 pairs of legs
spinneret
Spider
abdomen

Word Bank

head	thorax	abdomen
cephalothorax	3 pair of legs	spinneret
4 pairs of legs	wings	

©1994 Instructional Fair, Inc.   48   IF0228 Life Science

The Worker Bee

Name _____

Label the parts of the worker bee.

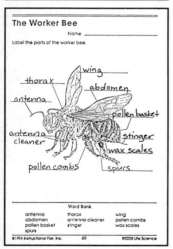

wing
thorax — abdomen
antenna
pollen basket
antenna cleaner
stinger
wax scales
pollen combs
spurs

Word Bank

antenna	thorax	wing
abdomen	antenna cleaner	pollen combs
pollen basket	stinger	wax scales
spurs		

©1994 Instructional Fair, Inc.   49   IF0228 Life Science

The Life Cycle of a Bee

Name _____

Label the stages of a bee's life cycle.

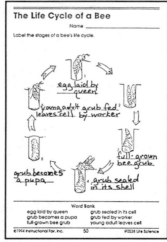

egg laid by queen
young adult leaves cell
grub fed by worker
full-grown bee grub
grub becomes a pupa
grub sealed in its shell

Word Bank

egg laid by queen	grub sealed in its cell
grub becomes a pupa	grub fed by worker
full-grown bee grub	young adult leaves cell

©1994 Instructional Fair, Inc.   50   IF0228 Life Science

The Life Cycle of an Ant

Name _____

Label the four stages of an ant's life cycle.

adult
pupa — eggs
larvae

Word Bank

eggs	adult	larvae	pupa

©1994 Instructional Fair, Inc.   51   IF0228 Life Science

The Grasshopper's Life Cycle

Name _____

The grasshopper's life cycle is an example of gradual metamorphosis. Label the steps of this cycle.

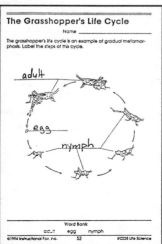

adult
egg
nymph

Word Bank

adult	egg	nymph

©1994 Instructional Fair, Inc.   52   IF0228 Life Science

Butterflies and Moths

Name _____

Butterflies and moths belong to the order of insects called Lepidoptera. Moths and butterflies each have some special characteristics to help you tell them apart. Label the parts of the butterfly. Label the special characteristics as either butterfly or moth.

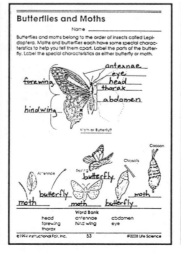

antennae
eye
head
thorax
forewing
abdomen
hindwing

Moth or Butterfly?

Antenna
Cocoon
Resting
Chrysalis
butterfly
moth
moth
butterfly
moth

Word Bank

head	antennae	abdomen
forewing	hind wing	eye
thorax		

©1994 Instructional Fair, Inc.   53   IF0228 Life Science

Metamorphosis

Name _____

Label the stages of Complete and Incomplete Metamorphosis.

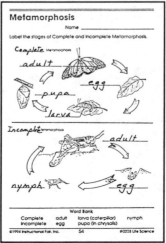

Complete Metamorphosis
adult
egg
pupa
larva

Incomplete Metamorphosis
adult
nymph
egg

Word Bank

Complete	adult	larva (caterpillar)	nymph
Incomplete	egg	pupa (in chrysalis)	

©1994 Instructional Fair, Inc.   54   IF0228 Life Science

The Clam

Name _____

Label the parts of the clam.

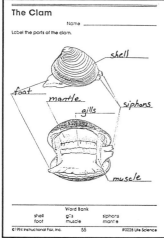

shell
foot
mantle
gills
siphons
muscle

Word Bank

shell	gills	siphons
foot	muscle	mantle

©1994 Instructional Fair, Inc.   55   IF0228 Life Science

The Starfish

Name _____

Label the parts of the starfish.

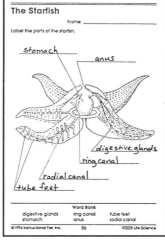

stomach
anus
digestive glands
ring canal
radial canal
tube feet

Word Bank

digestive glands	ring canal	tube feet
stomach	anus	radial canal

©1994 Instructional Fair, Inc.   56   IF0228 Life Science

The Sponge

Name _____

Label the parts of the sponge.

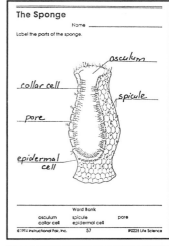

osculum
collar cell
spicule
pore
epidermal cell

Word Bank

osculum	spicule	pore
collar cell	epidermal cell	

©1994 Instructional Fair, Inc.   57   IF0228 Life Science

The Hydra

Name _____

Label the parts of the hydra.

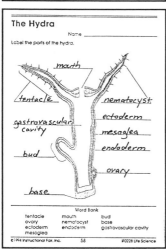

mouth
tentacle
nematocyst
gastrovascular cavity
ectoderm
mesoglea
endoderm
bud
ovary
base

Word Bank

tentacle	mouth	bud
ovary	nematocyst	base
ectoderm	endoderm	gastrovascular cavity
mesoglea		

©1994 Instructional Fair, Inc.   58   IF0228 Life Science

The Planarian

Name _____

A planarian is a small flatworm that can regenerate missing body parts when portions are cut off.

Label the parts of the regenerated planarian.

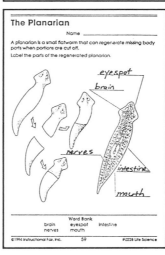

eyespot
brain
nerves
intestine
mouth

Word Bank

brain	eyespot	intestine
nerves	mouth	

©1994 Instructional Fair, Inc.   59   IF0228 Life Science

Worms

Name _____

A key is a tool used by scientists to help them identify living things. Use the key below to identify the worms on this page.

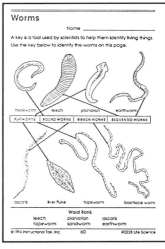

hookworm   leech   planarian   earthworm

| FLATWORMS | ROUND WORMS | RIBBON WORMS | SEGMENTED WORMS |

ascaris   liver fluke   tapeworm   bootlace worm

Word Bank

leech	planarian	ascaris
tapeworm	sandworm	earthworm

©1994 Instructional Fair, Inc.   60   IF0228 Life Science

The Earthworm

Name _____

Label the exterior parts of the earthworm.

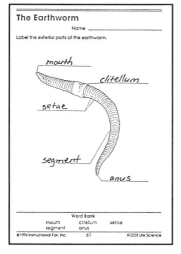

mouth
clitellum
setae
segment
anus

Word Bank

mouth	clitellum	setae
segment	anus	

©1994 Instructional Fair, Inc.   61   IF0228 Life Science

The Earthworm - Digestive System

Name _____

For the earthworm, as with most animals, digestion takes place in a long tube with openings at both ends. This tube is divided into organs that do different jobs.

Label the parts of the earthworm's digestive system.

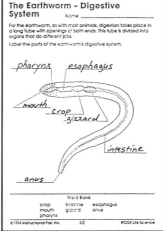

pharynx
esophagus
mouth
crop
gizzard
intestine
anus

Word Bank

crop	intestine	esophagus
mouth	gizzard	anus
pharynx		

©1994 Instructional Fair, Inc.   62   IF0228 Life Science

The Amoeba

Name _____

Label the parts of the reproducing amoeba.

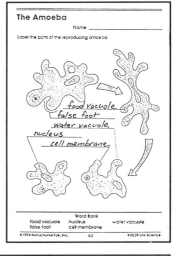

food vacuole
false foot
water vacuole
nucleus
cell membrane

Word Bank

food vacuole	nucleus	water vacuole
false foot	cell membrane	

©1994 Instructional Fair, Inc.   63   IF0228 Life Science

The Euglena

Name _____

Label the parts of the euglena.

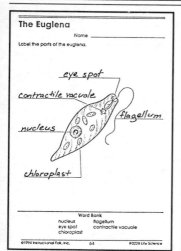

eye spot
contractile vacuole
flagellum
nucleus
chloroplast

Word Bank
nucleus   flagellum
eye spot   contractile vacuole
chloroplast

©1994 Instructional Fair, Inc.   64   IF0228 Life Science

The Paramecium

Name _____

Label the parts of the reproducing paramecium.

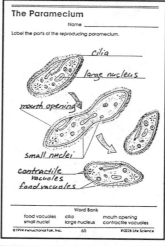

cilia
large nucleus
mouth opening
small nuclei
contractile vacuoles
food vacuoles

Word Bank
food vacuoles   cilia   mouth opening
small nuclei   large nucleus contractile vacuoles

©1994 Instructional Fair, Inc.   65   IF0228 Life Science

The Growth of a Yeast Cell

Name _____

Label the parts of this growing yeast cell. Number the steps in the correct order.

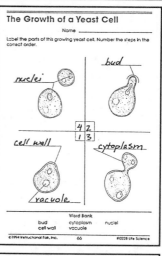

nuclei
bud
cell wall

| 4 | 2 |
| 1 | 3 |

cytoplasm
vacuole

Word Bank
bud   cytoplasm   nuclei
cell wall   vacuole

©1994 Instructional Fair, Inc.   66   IF0228 Life Science

Find the Missing Link

Name _____

Write the missing organism in each food chain.

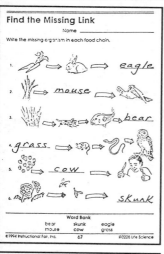

1. → eagle
2. → mouse →
3. → bear
4. grass → → →
5. → cow →
6. → → skunk

Word Bank
bear   skunk   eagle
mouse   cow   grass

©1994 Instructional Fair, Inc.   67   IF0228 Life Science

Producers and Consumers

Name _____

Organisms are either producers or consumers, depending upon the source of their energy. Consumers are either herbivores, carnivores or omnivores. Label the producers, omnivores, herbivores and carnivores in each food chain.

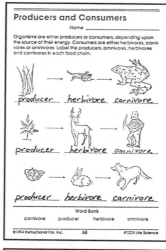

producer   herbivore   carnivore
producer   herbivore   omnivore
producer   herbivore   carnivore

Word Bank
carnivore   producer   herbivore   omnivore

©1994 Instructional Fair, Inc.   68   IF0228 Life Science

Food Web

Name _____

The organisms found in a typical food web are pictured below. Using arrows construct a food web. Label the organisms found in the food web.

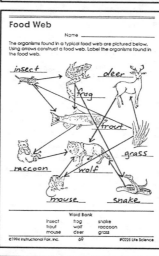

insect   deer
frog
trout
grass
raccoon   wolf
mouse   snake

Word Bank
insect   frog   snake
trout   wolf   raccoon
mouse   deer   grass

©1994 Instructional Fair, Inc.   69   IF0228 Life Science

Energy Pyramid

Name _____

Write the names of the organisms pictured on this page where they belong on the energy pyramid. Some may be listed on more than one level.

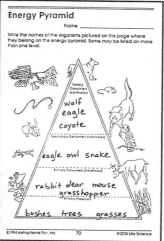

Tertiary Consumers (carnivores)
wolf
eagle
coyote

Secondary Consumers (carnivores)
eagle owl snake

Primary Consumers (herbivores)
rabbit deer mouse
grasshopper

Primary Producers
bushes trees grasses

©1994 Instructional Fair, Inc.   70   IF0228 Life Science

Biomes of North America

Name _____

Color the map and key to identify the major biomes of North America.

Tundra
Coniferous forest
Deciduous forest
Tropical rain forest
Grassland
Desert

©1994 Instructional Fair, Inc.   71   IF0228 Life Science

Vegetation Layers

Name _____

A mature forest has several layers of vegetation. Each layer supports a different kind of animal life.

Label the five layers of vegetation in the forest pictured on this page. List two animals that live in each layer.

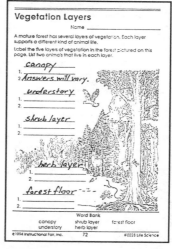

canopy
1.
2. Answers will vary.
understory
1.
2.
shrub layer
1.
2.
herb layer
1.
2.
forest floor
1.
2.

Word Bank
canopy   shrub layer   forest floor
understory   herb layer

©1994 Instructional Fair, Inc.   72   IF0228 Life Science

The Frog – Internal

Name _____

Label the parts of the frog.

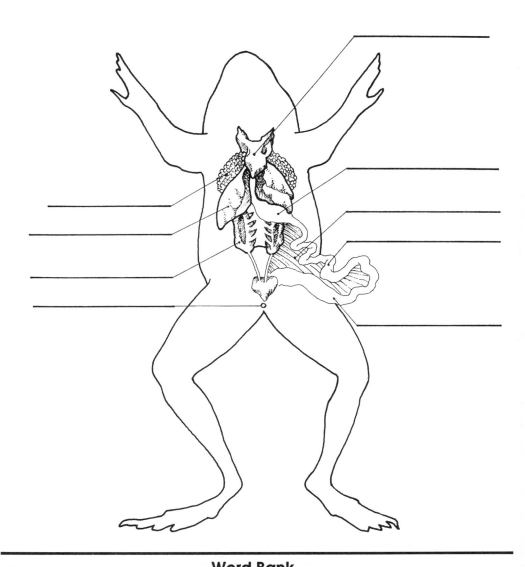

Word Bank

heart	lung	mesentery
kidney	anus	small intestine
stomach	liver	large intestine

Life Cycle of a Frog

Name _____

Label the steps in the life cycle of the frog.

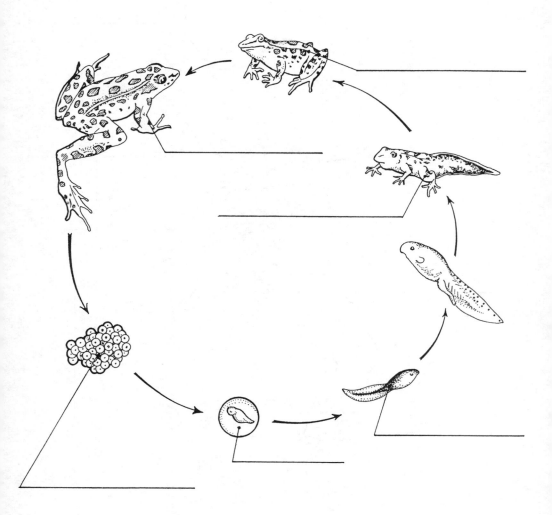

Pit Viper Snake

Name _____

Label the parts of the head of the pit viper snake.

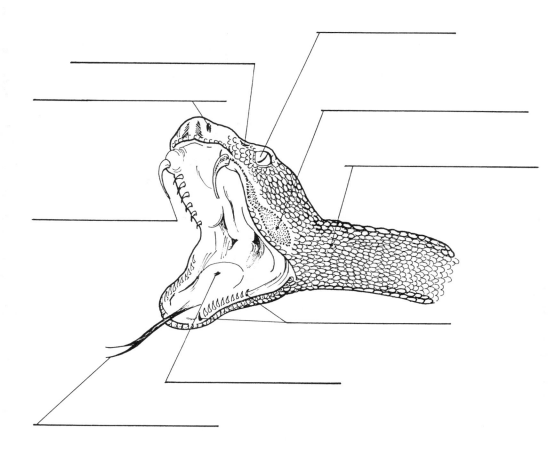

Word Bank

eye	pit	nostril
fang	teeth	tongue
glottis (windpipe)	venom sac	scaly skin

The Parts of a Bird

Name _____

Label the parts of the bird.

Word Bank

crown   secondaries   primaries
belly   breast   throat
tail feathers back   bill

Feathered Friend's Feet

Name _____

A bird's feet can tell you many things about its habits or home.
How do each of these birds use their feet in a special way?

_____

_____

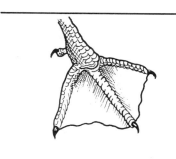

_____

_____

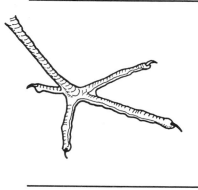

_____

Word Bank
for perching on branches
for wading in mud
for grasping in order to climb
for swimming
for catching prey

Bird Bills

Name _____

The shape of a bird's bill can often tell what the bird eats. How do each of these birds use their bills in a special way to eat food?

_____

_____

_____

_____

_____

_____

Word Bank

- for pounding holes to find insects
- to tear the flesh of animals
- to scoop large mouthfuls of water and fish
- to suck nectar from flowers
- to stab small fish
- to crack open seeds

Strangers in the Night

Name _____

It's much easier to identify a bird when you can see its coloring, size and shape. At night this is usually difficult.

See if you can identify these birds by their silhouettes.

Word Bank

kingfisher	pheasant	barn swallow
great blue heron	cardinal	horned owl
robin	pelican	hummingbird
blue jay		

Highways for Birds

Name _____

Label each of these major flyways found in North America.

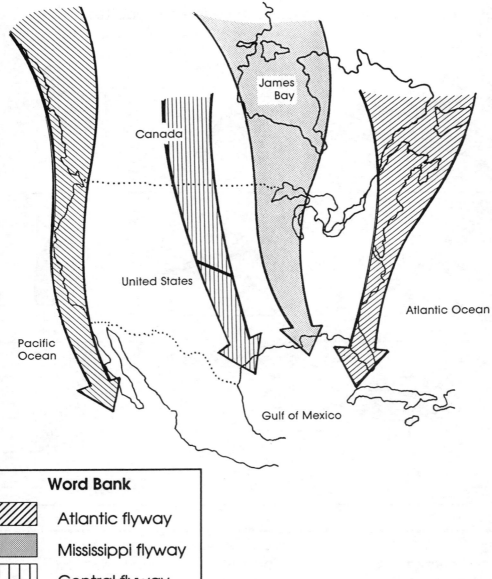

Canada

James Bay

United States

Pacific Ocean

Atlantic Ocean

Gulf of Mexico

Word Bank

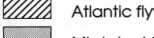 Atlantic flyway

Mississippi flyway

 Central flyway

Pacific flyway

Chicken Egg

Name _____

Label the parts of this fertilized hen's egg.

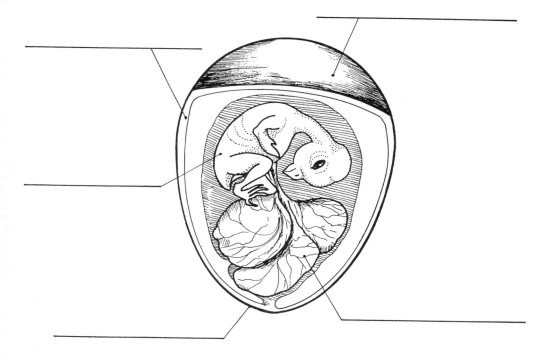

Word Bank

membrane	air space	embryo
yolk sac	shell	

The Crayfish

Name _____

Label the parts of the crayfish.

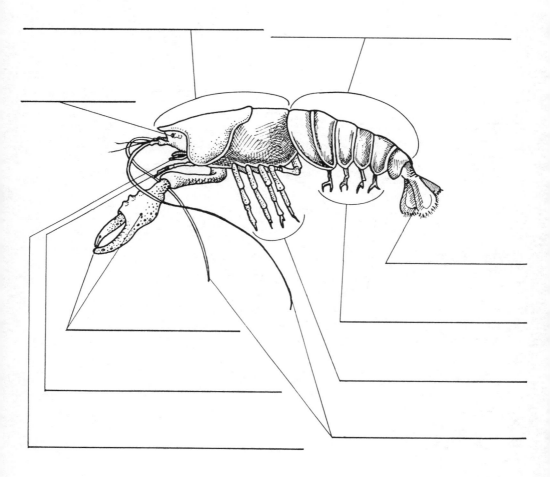

Word Bank

eye	walking legs	flipper
swimmerets	abdomen	antennae
cephalothorax	cheliped	maxilliped
mandible		

Insect Orders

Name _____

The major groups of insects are called orders. Below are examples from seven of the most common orders of insects. Label each insect and its order.

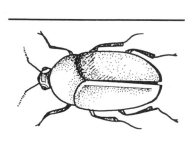

_____

_____

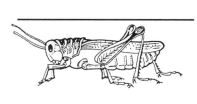

_____

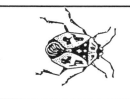

_____

_____

_____

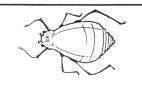

_____

Word Bank

- beetles (Coleoptera)
- flies (Diptera)
- grasshoppers (Orthoptera)
- leafhoppers (Homoptera)
- bees and wasps (Hymenoptera)
- butterflies and moths (Lepidoptera)
- true bugs (Hemiptera)

Spiders and Insects

Name _____

Spiders are not insects. Label the parts of the spider and insect.

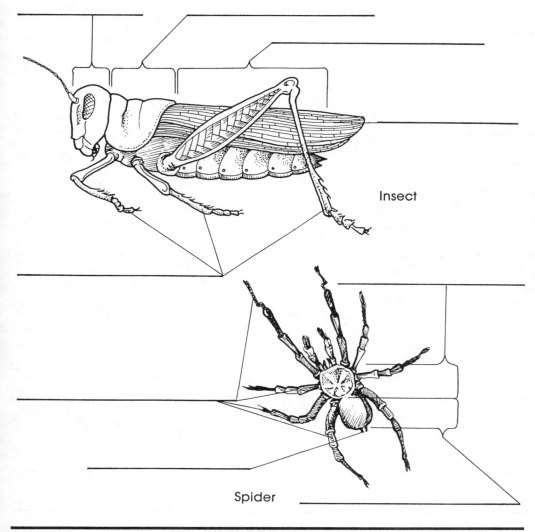

Insect

Spider

Word Bank

head	thorax	abdomen
cephalothorax	3 pairs of legs	spinneret
4 pairs of legs	wings	

The Worker Bee

Name _____

Label the parts of the worker bee.

Word Bank

antenna	thorax	wing
abdomen	antenna cleaner	pollen combs
pollen basket	stinger	wax scales
spurs		

The Life Cycle of a Bee

Name _____

Label the stages of a bee's life cycle.

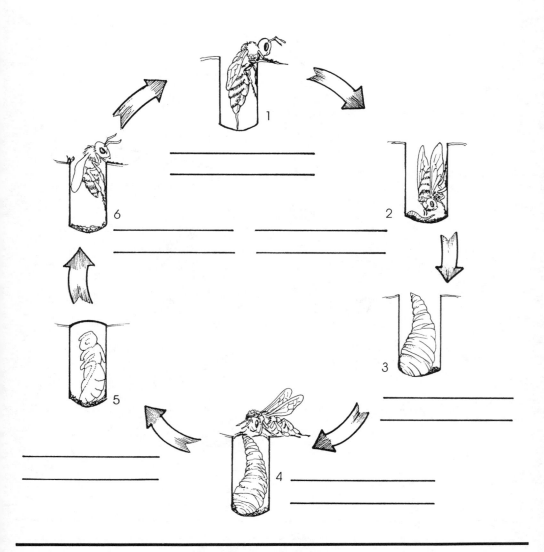

Word Bank

egg laid by queen   grub sealed in its cell
grub becomes a pupa   grub fed by worker
full-grown bee grub   young adult leaves cell

The Life Cycle of an Ant

Name _____

Label the four stages of an ant's life cycle.

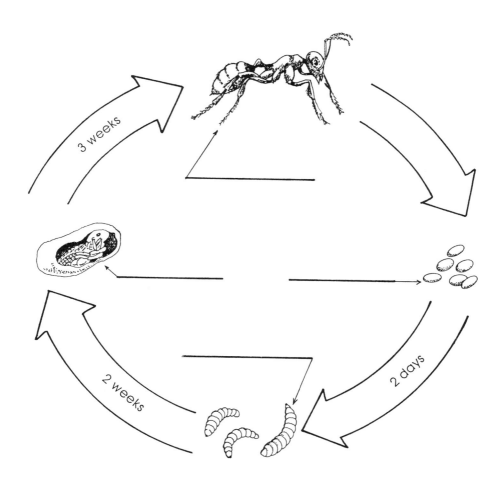

Word Bank

eggs   adult   larvae   pupa

The Grasshopper's Life Cycle

Name _____

The grasshopper's life cycle is an example of gradual metamorphosis. Label the steps of this cycle.

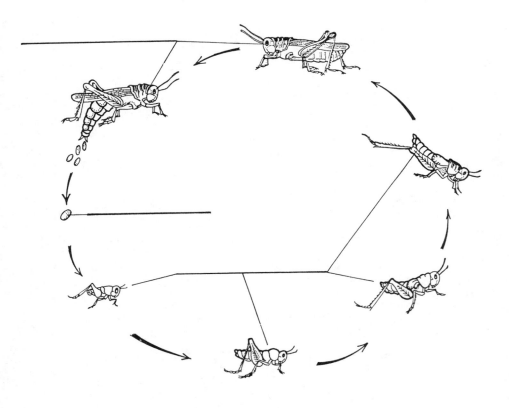

Word Bank

adult   egg   nymph

Butterflies and Moths

Name _____

Butterflies and moths belong to the order of insects called Lepidoptera. Moths and butterflies each have some special characteristics to help you tell them apart. Label the parts of the butterfly. Label the special characteristics as either butterfly or moth.

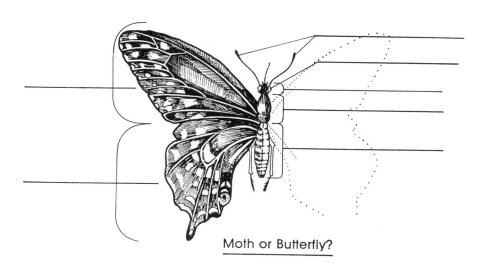

Moth or Butterfly?

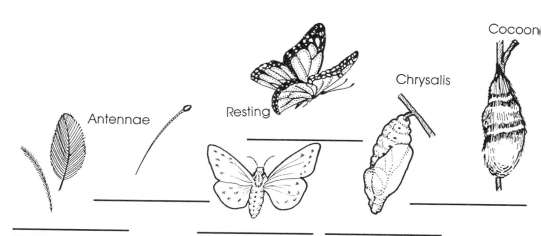

Cocoon

Chrysalis

Antennae

Resting

Word Bank

head	antennae	abdomen
forewing	hind wing	eye
thorax		

Metamorphosis

Name _____

Label the stages of Complete and Incomplete Metamorphosis.

_____ Metamorphosis

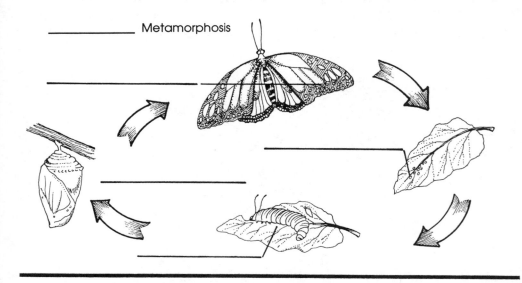

_____ Metamorphosis

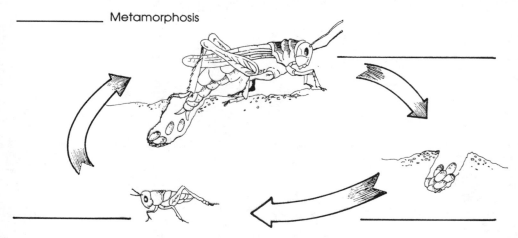

Word Bank

Complete	adult	larva (caterpillar)	nymph
Incomplete	egg	pupa (in chrysalis)	

The Clam

Name _____

Label the parts of the clam.

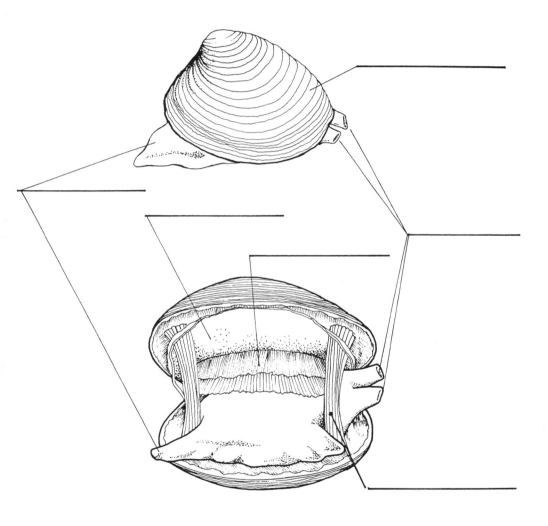

Word Bank

shell	gills	siphons
foot	muscle	mantle

The Starfish

Name _____

Label the parts of the starfish.

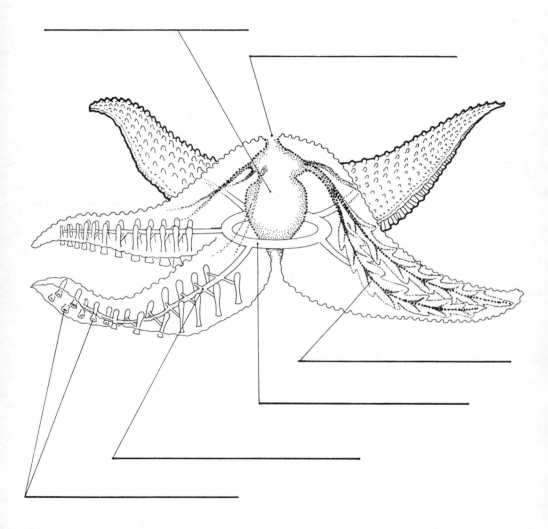

Word Bank

digestive glands   ring canal   tube feet
stomach   anus   radial canal

The Sponge

Name _____

Label the parts of the sponge.

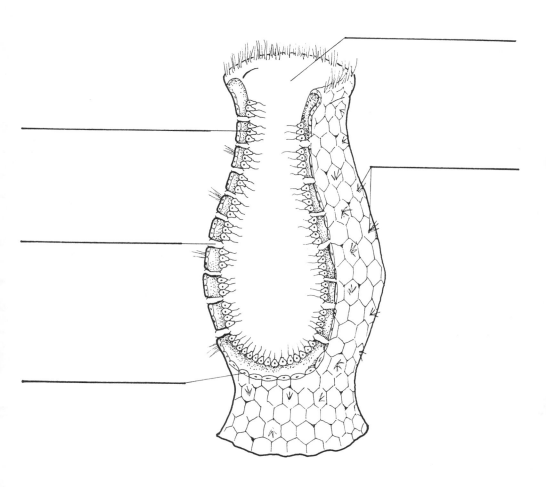

The Hydra

Name _____

Label the parts of the hydra.

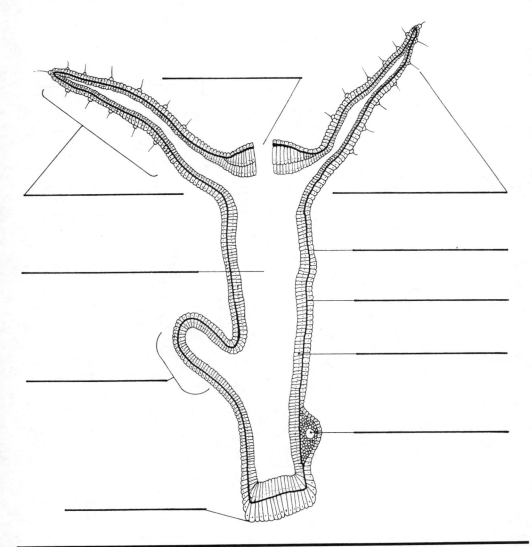

Word Bank

tentacle	mouth	bud
ovary	nematocyst	base
ectoderm	endoderm	gastrovascular cavity
mesoglea		

The Planarian

Name _____

A planarian is a small flatworm that can regenerate missing body parts when portions are cut off.

Label the parts of the regenerated planarian.

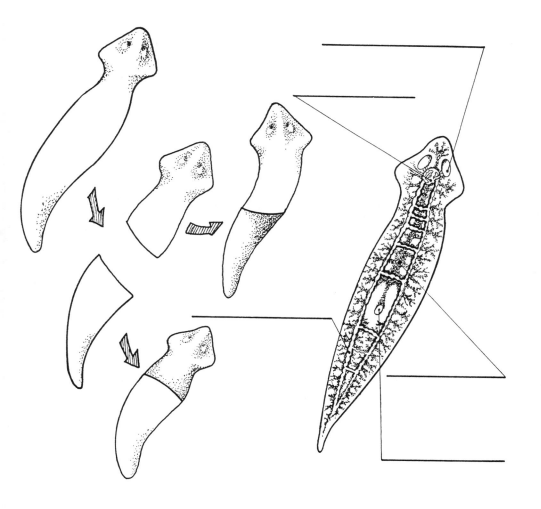

Word Bank

brain	eyespot	intestine
nerves	mouth	

Worms

Name _____

A key is a tool used by scientists to help them identify living things.
Use the key below to identify the worms on this page.

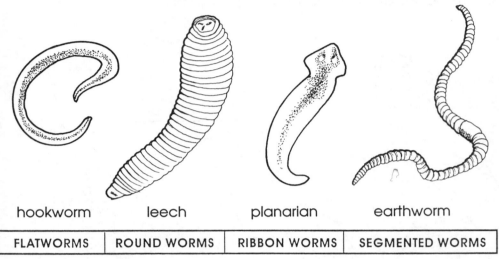

| hookworm | leech | planarian | earthworm |

| FLATWORMS | ROUND WORMS | RIBBON WORMS | SEGMENTED WORMS |

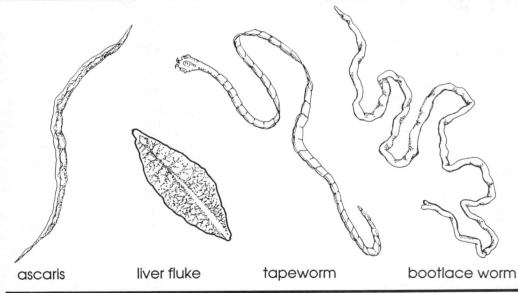

| ascaris | liver fluke | tapeworm | bootlace worm |

Word Bank

| leech | planarian | ascaris |
| tapeworm | sandworm | earthworm |

The Earthworm

Name _____

Label the exterior parts of the earthworm.

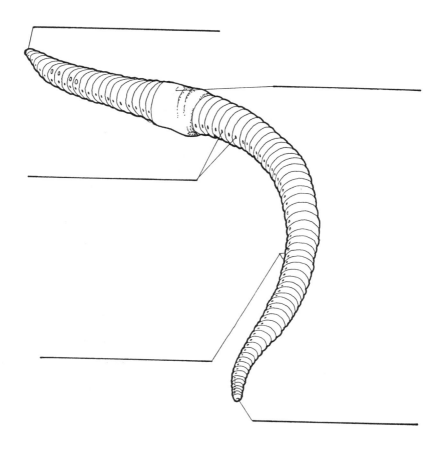

Word Bank

mouth	clitellum	setae
segment	anus	

The Earthworm – Digestive System

Name _____

For the earthworm, as with most animals, digestion takes place in a long tube with openings at both ends. This tube is divided into organs that do different jobs.

Label the parts of the earthworm's digestive system.

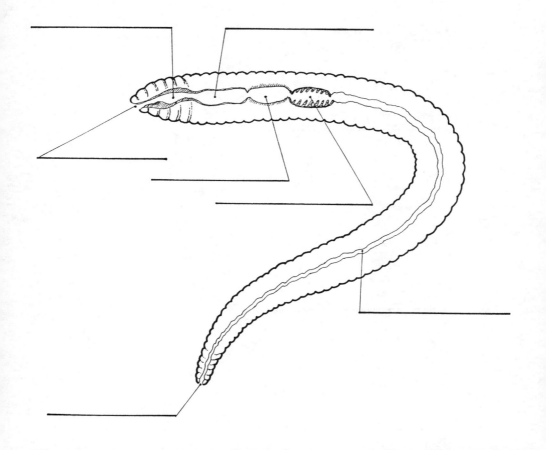

Word Bank

crop	intestine	esophagus
mouth	gizzard	anus
pharynx		

The Amoeba

Name _____

Label the parts of the reproducing amoeba.

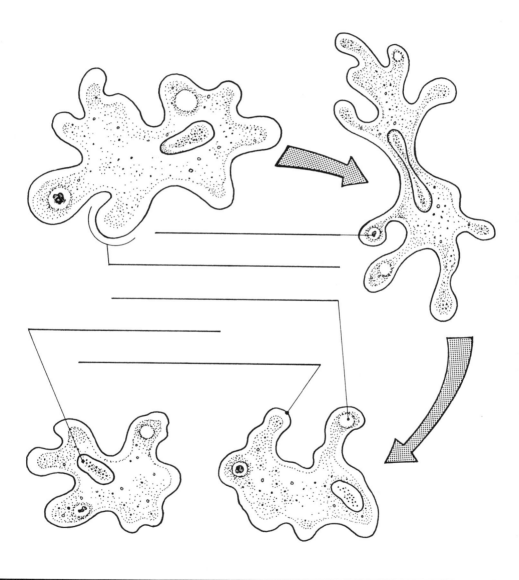

Word Bank

food vacuole	nucleus	water vacuole
false foot	cell membrane	

The Euglena

Name _____

Label the parts of the euglena.

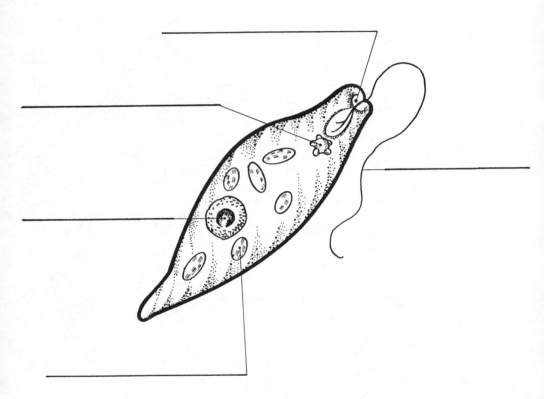

Word Bank

nucleus   flagellum
eye spot   contractile vacuole
chloroplast

The Paramecium

Name _____

Label the parts of the reproducing paramecium.

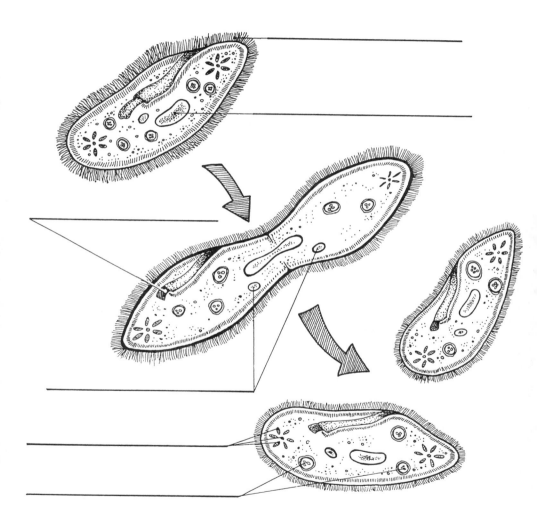

Word Bank

food vacuoles	cilia	mouth opening
small nuclei	large nucleus	contractile vacuoles

The Growth of a Yeast Cell

Name _____

Label the parts of this growing yeast cell. Number the steps in the correct order.

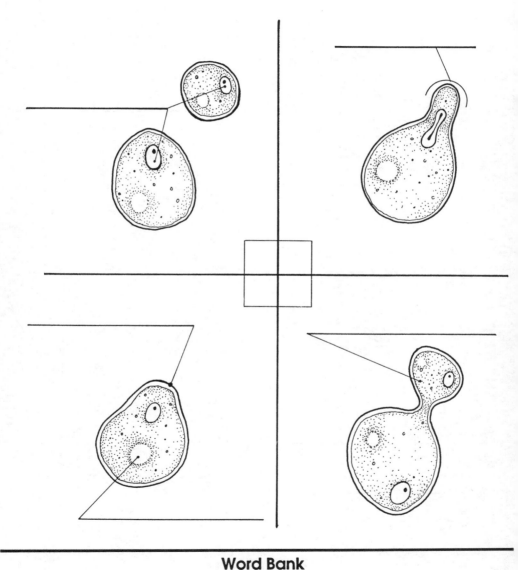

Word Bank

bud	cytoplasm	nuclei
cell wall	vacuole	

Find the Missing Link

Name _____

Write the missing organism in each food chain.

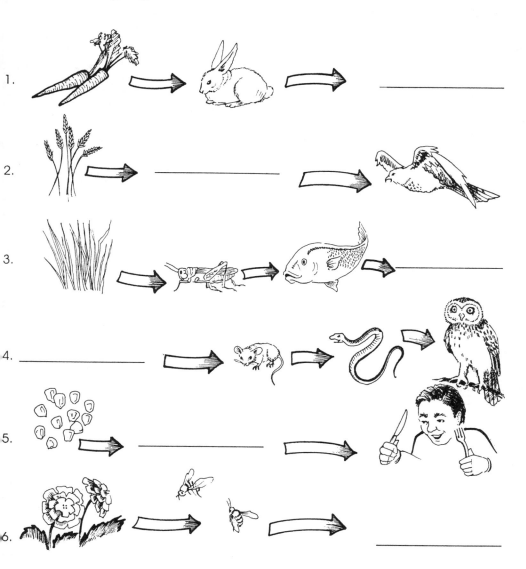

1.

2.

3.

4.

5.

6.

Producers and Consumers

Name _____

Organisms are either producers or consumers, depending upon the source of their energy. Consumers are either herbivores, carnivores or omnivores. Label the producers, omnivores, herbivores and carnivores in each food chain.

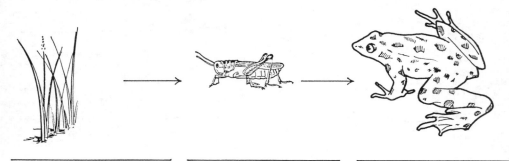

_____   _____   _____

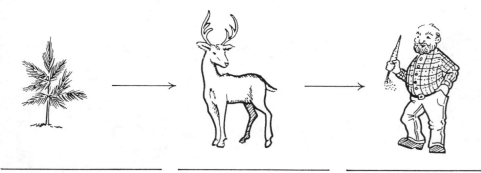

_____   _____   _____

_____   _____   _____

Word Bank

carnivore   producer   herbivore   omnivore

Food Web

Name _____

The organisms found in a typical food web are pictured below.
Using arrows construct a food web. Label the organisms found in
the food web.

Word Bank

insect	frog	snake
trout	wolf	raccoon
mouse	deer	grass

Energy Pyramid

Name _____

Write the names of the organisms pictured on this page where they belong on the energy pyramid. Some may be listed on more than one level.

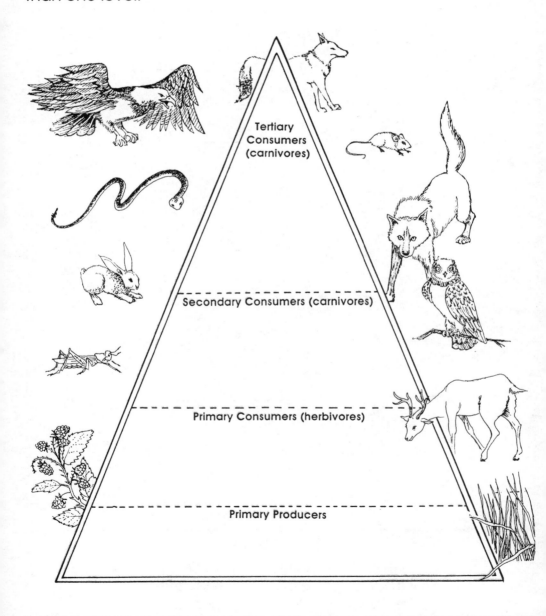

Biomes of North America

Name _____

Color the map and key to identify the major biomes of North America.

Tundra
Coniferous forest
Deciduous forest
Tropical rain forest
Grassland
Desert

Vegetation Layers

Name _____

A mature forest has several layers of vegetation. Each layer supports a different kind of animal life.

Label the five layers of vegetation in the forest pictured on this page. List two animals that live in each layer.

_____
1. _____
2. _____

_____
1. _____
2. _____

_____
1. _____
2. _____

_____
1. _____
2. _____

_____
1. _____
2. _____

Word Bank

canopy	shrub layer	forest floor
understory	herb layer	